Nurturing Your Family With Yoga

Nurturing Your Family With Yoga

Dr Kiki Morriss

YOGAWORDS

For John, Kai, Rafferty and Florence

Nurturing Your Family With Yoga: An A-Z of yoga poses, meditations, breathing and games for the whole family

First published by YogaWords, an imprint of Pinter & Martin, 2021

All photographs © 2021 Vanessa Berberian Photography
www.vanessaberberian.com

ISBN 978-1-906756-80-2

Also available as an ebook

British Library Cataloguing-in-Publication Data
A catalogue record for this book is available from the British Library.

Set in Queulat
Designed by Blok Graphic, London

Printed and bound in Poland by Hussar Books

This book has been printed on paper that is sourced and harvested from sustainable forests and is FSC accredited.

Pinter & Martin Ltd
6 Effra Parade
London SW2 1PS

yogawords.com

Contents

About the author

Kiki Morriss was born in London and fell in love with yoga aged six, when she took a class in a friend's playroom. She has worked as a medical doctor in some of London's top hospitals and writes a regular column on anatomy for Om Yoga magazine.

She started her yoga career teaching two-year-olds, taught yoga therapy at London's celebrated Triyoga and is the founder of Primrose Hill Yoga. Known for her 'beautiful, calming voice', she has narrated Becalmed, an album of Yoga Nidra meditations.

She lives in London with her husband and their three children.

Becalmed Yoga Nidra is available on Spotify, Amazon Music and iTunes.
You can visit Kiki at **primrosehillyoga.com** or Instagram **@kiki.yoga**

My yoga journey

In this book I share the practices I've developed during my twenty years of teaching yoga to children and families, along with useful tips to help you instil a lifelong love of yoga in your children.

I took my first yoga class in a friend's playroom when I was six years old and the memory of that wonderful day has served as the inspiration for my passion and commitment to finding innovative, creative and authentic ways to share yoga with children – in schools, yoga studios and at home with my own family. I want children to enjoy yoga because I know how incredibly good it is for them and how great it can make them feel!

Teaching yoga to children is often a challenge, as they can be unwilling and unfocused. The practices in this book are my tried and tested ways of getting them interested and engaged. When it works it is like some kind of alchemy and feels transformative for everyone.

"I want children to enjoy yoga because I know how incredibly good it is for them and how great it can make them feel."

The hardest part of a home yoga practice is getting started and we are all full of excuses! Our house is a mess, the children are arguing, we're tired, we're short of space, it's not the right time... It's important to remember that you can begin with just one yoga pose or a single breath in and out. It really is that simple. Start small and marvel as your family practice grows and gives back to you all.

My yoga journey, from childhood to adulthood, has been one of the most beautiful experiences of my life and this ancient practice never fails to nurture or strengthen my family and me.

I wish you and your family an equally joyful yoga journey.

"You can begin with just one yoga pose or a single breath in and out. It really is that simple."

Your introduction to yoga

T he word 'yoga' comes from the ancient Indian language of Sanskrit and means 'to reconnect'. The practice of yoga, involving poses, breathing exercises and meditation, will connect you with your innate ability to nurture yourself and, in turn, with your innate ability to nurture the children in your care.

Through yoga we listen deeply to our bodies and minds, we observe our breath, let go of the cares of the day and become truly present. We develop an attitude of clarity and calm, creating the space required to listen to our own needs and the needs of our children. We accept who they are and take care of them gently and wisely, as they grow into themselves.

As parents we want our children to be happy and our homes to be harmonious. Yoga gives simple, practical tools to achieve just that, teaching us that happiness is our natural state and guiding us towards reconnecting to our true, joyful selves.

By introducing your children to yoga you are giving them a gift for life, as it will help them build a strong and flexible body, achieve a peaceful and relaxed state of mind, sleep well, build their self-confidence and improve their focus, concentration and memory. By practising together as a family, you will strengthen the bond and trust between you all.

"Family yoga presents an opportunity for everyone to benefit from some slow, quiet, considered time together. Phones and screens are switched off."

Modern family life can be hectic and exhausting, with busy schedules as well as academic, social and online pressures. Family yoga presents an opportunity for everyone to benefit from some slow, quiet, considered time together. Phones and screens are switched off. Bodies are stretched, the breath is steadied, stresses are released and the positive connection and mutual respect between family members is strengthened.

I believe that the family is the single most important influence in a child's life and that family yoga can play a key role in bringing yoga to the heart of a home. As a medical doctor, yoga teacher and yoga therapist, I know this early exposure to yoga lays the foundations for the teen and adult years, acting as powerful, preventative medicine and supporting good mental, physical and emotional health throughout life.

Your guide to using this book

This book is designed for you and your children to open on any page and be inspired.

In the A–Z section there are 26 poses, each beginning with a different letter of the alphabet. For every pose there are instructions, a list of benefits, a visualisation and an affirmation. For some of the poses there are additional games, breathing exercises, guided meditations, adjustments, reflections and variations. You can practise the poses individually and find out which of the activities attached to each pose you and your children are interested in.

When you have practised all 26 poses, play the A–Z of Yoga game on page 107, which is a firm favourite with children. Another popular game is the Detective Yoga game on page 108.

You can also do my family's favourite routines, the Sun Salutation and Yoga in Bed sequences, as well as having fun with the partner yoga poses and storytelling using yoga poses.

"This book is designed for you and your children to open on any page and be inspired."

Benefits

Your children will receive many benefits from yoga. Angel Wings will stretch and increase the flexibility of their shoulders, as well as opening their chest and helping them to breathe well. It's a good antidote after they have sat at a desk or computer. Butterfly will open their hips, stretch their inner thighs and calm their minds. Crow is a challenging balance that will develop their strength, concentration and determination.

Ask your children how each pose makes them feel, both physically and mentally. Ask them where their body is stretching and where it is becoming stronger. Ask them which are their favourite poses and the reasons why.

"Ask your children how each pose makes them feel, both physically and mentally."

Affirmations

Affirmations are positively worded statements, such as 'I am kind', 'I am grateful' or 'I am determined'. They are powerful tools to create a positive attitude and inner dialogue, to boost self-esteem and develop confidence. They are optional and can be repeated, either silently or aloud, as you and your children hold the poses.

Visualisations

Many yoga poses are named after and inspired by animals and nature. The visualisations for each pose will encourage your children to be playful and imaginative as they become a pride of ferocious lions, a forest of trees, a meadow of butterflies or a group of jellyfish floating in the deep ocean. The ability to visualise and to create mental imagery has been shown to reduce anxiety and build resilience in young people.

 This symbol will guide you to the visualisation for each pose in the A-Z section

Breathing

Awareness of your breath lies at the heart of a yoga practice, as the way you breathe has a direct effect on your thoughts, feelings, actions and health. When you breathe steadily, you become energised and relaxed, you work and sleep well and you strengthen and balance your nervous system, so you are ready for all the ups and downs of life and can recover easily from them. Your breath will always be with you and helping your children to be aware of and in control of the way they breathe is like introducing them to a lifelong, loyal friend.

As your children are discovering the yoga postures, encourage them to breathe slowly, gently and steadily. In Oyster and Queen Cleopatra ask them to move their bodies in time with their breath. This practice of synchronising breath and movement has a soothing, calming effect. The simple breathing exercises for Lion, Mouse, Namasté, Oyster, Queen Cleopatra, Rabbit, Snail, Volcano, X Marks the Spot, Y is for Yoga and Savasana can easily be made a part of your everyday life and will have a profound effect on your wellbeing as a family.

Reflections

Yoga poses can be the starting point for interesting and thoughtful discussions between you and your children. The reflections will inspire and inform these conversations.

Adjustments

Adjustments are ways that you can gently help each other to stretch your bodies a little more, to improve your posture or to relax. Children love to adjust their parents and siblings. It is important to adjust each other gently.

Variations

There are many different ways to do a yoga pose. For instance, Tree is usually done standing upright but can also be done lying on your back. The variations will show you some alternative ways of doing the poses.

Guided meditations

Meditation is a practice that focuses the mind on a particular thought, object or activity and helps you to become more aware, calm and present.

The guided meditation linked to Butterfly pose will take your children on a journey to their favourite place. The 'Where is the butterfly?' meditation is a soothing, relaxing practice and will help to calm and focus your children when they feel scattered, upset or overwhelmed. The meditation linked to Kite pose will make them more aware of the nature of their mind and how difficult it is to concentrate on one thing

for a sustained period of time. It will teach them to be more aware of their own body and mind.

Ask your children to close their eyes and then read the meditations to them slowly. Talk to them afterwards about their experience of the meditation. This will build their confidence and ability to articulate and express themselves. If you have more than one child, it will encourage them to listen to and respect their siblings, introducing the concepts of kindness and generosity, of sharing the attention with the people we are with.

Savasana

At the end of the A–Z section, you and your children are introduced to Savasana, where you lie on your back, close your eyes and rest. This is the most important yoga pose of all and is a wonderful way to start or finish a family yoga session – quiet, peaceful, calm and together.

"Children love to adjust their parents and siblings. It is important to adjust each other gently."

Tips for sharing yoga successfully with children

Children's yoga is playful and full of life, when compared to the serene environment of an adults' class. Here are my top tips for a happy, successful time practising together as a family.

1. The first thing I teach children and families is a pose beginning with the first letter of their name. This always interests them. Then we spell out their names using the yoga poses.

2. As a family we practise yoga everywhere we go. We practise Sleeping Butterfly in bed, Tree in the forest, Jellyfish or Oyster at the seaside, Snail in the garden, Giraffe or Lion at the zoo or Angel Wings when someone is feeling sad and needs some love and care. Making your practice spontaneous and relevant to where you are and what is happening in your lives will help your children engage with yoga naturally and easily.

3. Find poses that reflect your children's interests. If they like insects, show them Butterfly. If they are fascinated by sea life, practise Jellyfish or Oyster. If they love wild animals, try Eagle or Lion and if they prefer the great outdoors, suggest Volcano.

4. Make your family practice light-hearted and brief. Follow the instructions for each pose or activity, but don't worry if your children are focused one minute and uninterested the next. This is natural and to be expected. Let your children do what they

want and don't put pressure on them to practise. Yoga will gradually improve their ability to concentrate.

5. Ask your children to choose a yoga pose for every year they have been alive and then arrange them into a sequence that flows naturally from one pose to the next. Think about what your bodies are doing in the different poses – forward

bending, back bending, side bending, twisting, balancing, and stretching.

6. Children love balancing poses. See how long they can balance in Tree while brushing their teeth or waiting for the bus. Count how many seconds they can lift one foot and then both feet in Crow. Hold hands in Dancer or Tree and notice how this helps you to balance for longer than if you were doing it alone. Try holding yoga balances with your eyes closed. You will need to rely on the receptors in your muscles and joints that are sending messages to your brain about where your body is in the space. This is called proprioception. The more you practise this the better your balance will get and the less likely you will lose your balance and fall over when you are older.

7. Invite friends over and teach them the A–Z of Yoga game and the Detective Yoga game. Host a yoga birthday party. Play pass the parcel and put an image of a yoga pose between each layer of wrapping. Play musical statues and when the music stops call out a yoga pose for everyone to come into. Tell a popular story using the yoga poses.

8. Children enjoy creating their own versions of yoga poses. Encourage this, as having fun and connecting with your children is more important than creating a perfect home practice.

9. Be patient and remember that a single, short-lived pose experienced one day may be the seed that grows into a lifelong love of yoga. Let it be full of joy and happiness!

10. Encourage your children to be considerate and respectful towards each other when they are practising yoga. Siblings can teach each other to be generous, thoughtful, fair, cooperative and kind. A family yoga practice will help you to nurture these qualities in your children, so they value, support and care for one another, both now and throughout their lives.

11. Share the breathing exercises with your children. When your breath and your mind are steady, you can be an unmovable mountain for them, regardless of how overwhelmed they feel in that moment. This puts you in the strongest position to help them learn how to calm and steady their own breath and mind.

12. Develop your own yoga practice. It is my personal practice that inspires my children the most and makes them want to join in, particularly if they can sit underneath or on top of me! It is also my own practice that gives me patience, perspective and a creative outlook when sharing yoga with children. When you experience your true, peaceful, joyful nature through the practice of yoga, you will be able to guide your children towards having the same experience.

13. If your children are interested in sports, introduce yoga to them as a way to warm up before playing and to cool down afterwards. Tell them that top footballers, surfers and skiers practice yoga to stretch and strengthen their muscles, to increase their flexibility and to sharpen their performance both physically and mentally.

14. Learn one new pose with your family every day. In less than a month you will be ready to play the A–Z of Yoga game.

15. Ask yourself how long you look at screens every day compared to the amount of time you give your full attention to your children. Use your family yoga practice to rebalance your priorities and refocus on your children. You will teach your children to be attentive by being attentive to them.

"You will teach your children to be attentive by being attentive to them."

Some practical advice

T hese suggestions will help you to create the foundation for your nurturing and nourishing family yoga practice. Follow the advice with an attitude of kindness and positivity, as you prepare to share yoga with your loved ones.

- Use blankets or rugs if you don't have yoga mats at home. If you would like to invest in a family supply of mats, I would recommend buying natural rubber ones rather than synthetic products. Let your children choose the colour of their own mat. Ask them to carefully roll up their own mat after using it. This will encourage them to be aware of and to care for their environment.

- Wear comfy clothes that you can move in easily and freely.

- It's fine to eat and drink a little before doing yoga but avoid a big meal just before you practise.

- Yoga can be practised at any time – morning, noon or night. Find the times that suit your family best.

- Create special spaces at home where you like to practise and that you associate with being peaceful, happy and together as a family.

Enjoy the ritual of preparing this space – perhaps lighting candles, spraying the area with a calming room spray or laying out the yoga mats in a special way.

- For Savasana, you can use cosy blankets to keep warm and lavender eye pillows to encourage your children to close their eyes, let go of their surroundings and allow themselves to be quiet, safe and aware of their inner world.

- Try playing music during your family yoga sessions. Ask your children to make suggestions. I play gentle, calm music during Savasana. Strong, upbeat music can be motivating for a more active yoga practice, as long as it's not too frenetic.

- Turn off your phones and computers so you are not distracted or disturbed. Give your children your full attention.

Yoga Nidra: a nurturing meditation

Practise this guided meditation before sharing the yoga practices in this book with your children, as to nurture them well you must start by nurturing yourself well. You can make a recording of your own voice, ask someone to read it to you or listen to the Becalmed Yoga Nidra recording available on Spotify, Amazon Music and iTunes.

You may also want to read it to your children, guiding them to be aware of their body and breath and to meditate on how they can take care of themselves physically, emotionally and mentally. If the practice is too long for them you can choose one part, such as the Creative Visualisations.

This Yoga Nidra practice is a simple yet profound way to unwind your nervous system and bring some calm into your daily life. Each step will guide you towards an experience of complete rest and relaxation.

1. Introduction

Lie on your back, sit in a chair or sit on the ground. Make yourself as comfortable as possible. Close your eyes and bring your awareness to your body. Be aware of the position of your body and how it feels right now. Be aware of the ground or the chair beneath you. Feel the touch of the air on your skin. Feel the touch of your clothing on your skin. As you lie or sit still, bring your awareness to your breath. Follow your natural breath in and your natural breath out. Be aware of the way your body moves as you breathe in and the way your body moves as you breathe out. Feel the expansion of your body as you breathe in. Feel the softening of your body as you breathe out. As you observe your breath, allow the cares of your day to wash away. Experience the reality of the present moment.

2. Awareness of Body

Become aware of your right big toe, second toe, third toe, fourth toe, fifth toe, top of foot, bottom of foot, ankle, shin, calf, front of knee, back of knee, front of thigh, back of thigh, hip.

Become aware of your left big toe, second toe, third toe, fourth toe, fifth toe, top of foot, bottom of foot, ankle, shin, calf, front of knee, back of knee, front of thigh, back of thigh, hip.

Become aware of your pelvis, buttocks, abdomen, chest, lower back, middle back, upper back, shoulders.

Right upper arm, elbow, forearm, wrist, back of hand, palm of hand, thumb, first finger, second finger, third finger, fourth finger.

Left upper arm, elbow, forearm, wrist, back of hand, palm of hand, thumb, first finger, second finger, third finger, fourth finger.

Become aware of your neck, jaw, chin, lips, teeth, tongue, cheeks, nose, eyes, eyelids, eyebrows, point between eyebrows, forehead, temples, top of head, back of head, ears.

3. Creative Visualisations

Imagine in your mind:

A wide, open, blue sky

Waves reaching the shore

Snow-covered mountains

A bird flying high in the sky

A winding river

A forest in springtime

A waterfall

A crescent moon in the sky

A butterfly landing on a flower

A rainbow in the sky

A vast ocean

A smiling face

A night-time sky of stars

Rest for 5–10 minutes, either in silence
or listening to some calm music.

4. Ending

To finish your meditation, become aware
of your body again. Become aware of the
floor or chair and the position of your body.
Observe your natural breath in and your
breath out. Bring your arms to either side
of your head and stretch your body from
your fingertips to your toes. Rest your arms
where it feels most comfortable for you.
Take your time. Do not hurry. Experience
this moment of rest and contentment.
When you are ready, open your eyes.

5. Nurturing Questions

Now ask yourself 'What can I do to nurture
myself? What can I do to take good care
of myself?'

Then ask yourself 'What can I do to nurture my
child? What can I do to take good care of my child?'
Ask yourself the same question for each one of
your children in turn.

Think about how you can nurture yourself and
your children physically, mentally, emotionally
and spiritually.

Write down your answers every time you practise
this meditation and use them to guide your words
and actions with clarity and purpose.

A to Z

Your yoga practices

When you have learned all these yoga poses from A-Z, you can play the game on page 107.

A is for Angel Wings
(Paschima Namaskarasana)

Benefits:

Opens your chest and encourages you to breathe well

Stretches and increases the flexibility of your shoulders

Flexes your wrists

Improves your posture

Affirmation:

I am kind.

1. Stand with your feet hip-width apart.

2. Bring your hands into a prayer position behind your back. If it is more comfortable, you can hold opposite elbows behind your back.

3. Close your eyes and take a few breaths in and out.

 Close your eyes and imagine you are an angel and your arms are your wings. Picture the colours and patterns of your wings clearly. Try drawing or painting them after your yoga session.

Reflections

Angels are loving, compassionate, kind and forgiving. Who do you know who needs help and kindness at the moment? Can you send them your positive thoughts and good wishes?

Kindness is the quality of being friendly, considerate and generous. How can you be kinder to yourself, the people in your life and your environment?

Notice how easy it is to round your back and bring your shoulders forward when you are sitting at a desk or computer. Angel Wings will help you to be aware of and to improve your posture.

Adjustment

Stand behind the person in Angel Wings. Place your hands on their shoulders and gently draw them back to help open their chest. Make sure they are keeping their pelvis in a neutral position and not over-arching their lower back.

B is for Butterfly (Baddha Konasana)

Benefits:

Opens your hips

Stretches your groin and inner thighs

Strengthens your back and abdomen

Relieves anxiety and tiredness

Calms and reassures you

Affirmation:

I am free.

1. Sit with the soles of your feet together and hold your ankles or feet.

2. Close your eyes and take a few steady breaths in and out.

 The Lifecycle of a Butterfly

Lie on your front and imagine you are a caterpillar. You are very hungry and crawl around, munching on all the delicious leaves. You grow bigger and bigger. Now come into Icicle pose (page 58) and slowly turn round and round, as you change into a chrysalis. When you have transformed into a chrysalis, you are very quiet, hanging from the underside of a leaf. Close your eyes and stand very still. Slowly you emerge from the chrysalis as a beautiful butterfly by coming into Butterfly pose. You dry your wings and then you are ready to spread them and take your first flight by lifting your knees up and down.

Reflections

The transformation of a caterpillar into a chrysalis and then finally into a butterfly is a miracle of nature. In an equally incredible way, you have changed and grown since you were a baby and you continue to change and grow every day. How do you feel about growing up and changing? It can feel exciting and scary at the same time.

Game

Play the Butterfly game. Sit in a circle in Butterfly pose. Choose a letter of the alphabet and take it in turns to say the name of a place that your butterfly is flying to that begins with that letter. It can be a village, town, country, continent or even another planet.

Guided meditation

'Sit in Butterfly pose. Close your eyes and imagine you are a butterfly. Keep the soles of your feet together and flap your butterfly wings by lifting your knees up and down. Imagine you can fly to a very special place, a place that you love to go to. Imagine arriving in that place. Picture in your mind where you are. Look around and notice everything you can see. Are there other people with you? Look up and notice what the sky looks like. What temperature is it? What can you feel under your feet? What is the weather like? Listen to the sounds you can hear. What would you like to do? You can spend time exploring or playing and doing whatever you like to do most in your special place. Notice how this place makes you feel. When you come here you feel very well and happy and full of good energy.

Now it is time to go back home. Begin to flap your wings again and imagine you are flying. Imagine you have arrived back. Picture your surroundings clearly. Take a deep breath in and out. Slowly open your eyes.'

'Where is the butterfly?' meditation

'Lie on your back in a comfortable position and close your eyes. Imagine a butterfly softly landing on your right foot, your left foot, right knee, left knee, right thigh, left thigh, your belly, chest, right shoulder, right arm, right hand, left shoulder, left arm, left hand, chin, nose, right cheek, left cheek, right eyelid, left eyelid, right eyebrow, left eyebrow, the point between your eyebrows, your forehead, the top of your head. Smile and imagine the butterfly flying away. Slowly open your eyes.'

As an alternative, you can close your eyes and ask a grown-up or friend to randomly and gently touch the different parts of your body listed above, asking you 'Where has the butterfly landed?' Tell them where you feel the butterfly on your body.

Variation

Sit in Butterfly and bend forwards. Bring your face towards your feet and your chest towards the ground. This position is called Star pose (Tarasana). Close your eyes and imagine you are a star shining bright in the night sky.

C is for Crow (Bakasana)

Benefits:

Strengthens your arms, wrists and hands

Focuses your mind

Develops balance, determination and stamina

Affirmation:

I am focused.

1. Bend your knees and come into a squatting position.

2. Place your palms flat on the ground with your fingers spread wide apart.

3. Rest your knees on your upper arms, as high as possible.

4. Lift and lower your right foot.

5. Lift and lower your left foot.

6. Lift both your feet and balance on your hands.

7. Bring your big toes together.

8. Stay in the balance for as long as you can.

9. Lower your feet to squat and circle your wrists in both directions.

 Imagine you are a crow balancing on the branch of a tree. Lift up one foot at a time and, with practice, you will be able to lift both feet.

Reflections

You will find some yoga poses easy and others will take more effort to master. Crow is a challenging pose and it may take time and consistent practice before you can confidently hold the balance.

The more demanding poses, such as Crow and Eagle, will teach you to cultivate persistence, perseverance and patience in all areas of your life, as you work towards what you want to achieve.

Make a clear mental image of yourself in Crow pose and then try the pose. This visualisation technique can be used to help you achieve the outcomes you want in your life.

Crows are extremely intelligent birds. They recognise human faces and remember who has threatened them and who has been kind to them. They are also able to make and use tools.

You are very intelligent as well – particularly when you are forgiving, compassionate, generous, resilient and positive.

D is for Dancer (Natarajasana)

Benefits:

Strengthens your legs and ankles

Stretches your chest, shoulders, arms and back

Develops good posture, balance and confidence

Focuses your mind

Affirmation:

I am graceful.

1. Stand with your feet together.

2. Bend your right knee and hold the inside edge of your right foot with your right hand.

3. Reach your left arm forwards and up.

4. Lift your right leg up and back, and press your right foot into your right hand.

5. Breathe in and out a few times.

6. Lower your right leg and left arm.

7. Repeat on the other side.

 Imagine you are a dancer. Dancers have stamina and grace. They are strong, creative, patient and dedicated. As you hold the pose feel these qualities in yourself.

Reflections

Try Dancer on your own and then try it holding hands with a friend. Is it easier to balance on your own or with someone else?

Do you know how to ask for and accept support when you need it? Are you aware when your parents, siblings, friends or teachers need help and are you willing to help them?

D

E is for Eagle (Garudasana)

Benefits:

Strengthens your ankles and legs

Stretches your shoulders and upper back

Develops flexibility and coordination

Focuses your mind

Optimises your brain function

1. Stand upright and bend both of your knees.

2. Cross your right thigh over your left thigh, wrap your right leg behind your left leg and tuck your toes on the inside of your left leg.

3. Cross your right upper arm over your left upper arm, wrap your forearms around each other and bring your palms together.

4. Squeeze your limbs together.

5. Breathe in and out a few times.

6. Repeat on the other side.

Affirmation:

I am determined.

 Eagles are symbols of courage, determination, leadership and grace. Adopt these attributes as you balance in Eagle pose. Imagine you can fly high and picture in your mind the earth below you.

Reflections

Your brain is divided into two hemispheres – your right brain and your left brain. The nerve fibres that join the two sides are known as the corpus callosum.

Your right brain governs the left side of your body and is associated with creativity, emotions and space-orientated tasks. Your left brain governs the right side of your body and is associated with logic, sequencing information and time-orientated tasks.

When you cross your arms and legs in Eagle pose, you bring body parts from one side of your body over to the other side. This action, known as crossing the midline, activates the corpus callosum and makes the two hemispheres of your brain communicate. Crossing the midline synchronises both sides of your body and both sides of your brain simultaneously. This allows your brain to function optimally.

Variation

Eagle can also be done lying on your back and this pose is called Eagle in the Nest. Lie down and come into Eagle. Breathe in. Breathe out and curl upwards, lifting your head, shoulders, upper back and legs. Breathe in and lower down. Remember to do the pose on both sides.

E

F is for Frog (Malasana)

Benefits:

Strengthens your legs and back

Stretches your hips and inner thighs

Improves your balance

Affirmation:

I am a miracle.

1. Squat with your feet slightly wider than hip-width apart.

2. Try to lower your heels down to the floor. Place a cushion under your heels if you can't bring them flat on the floor.

3. Place your hands on the floor in front of your feet.

4. Lift your upper body up and look forwards.

5. Breathe in and out a few times.

6. Stand up and shake out your legs.

 Come into Mouse pose (page 70) and imagine you are frogspawn in a pond, surrounded by bulrushes and weeping willows. You are a tiny egg with the potential to transform into a frog. Now imagine you are changing into a tadpole, as you lie on your front with your arms by your sides. Swim around the pond by wiggling from side to side. The pond is full of life - newts, dragonflies and pond skaters. Next imagine you are changing into a frog, as you squat in Frog pose. See how far you can jump with your long, powerful legs and make lots of noise 'Ribbit, ribbit, ribbit!'

Reflections

Frogs, like butterflies, symbolise the miracle of transformation, as they develop from tadpoles into froglets and finally into fully grown frogs.

You are also a miracle as you grow up and develop. Think about how you have developed from when you were a baby. Celebrate all the miraculous ways that you change and grow throughout your life. Do what you can to look after your amazing body and mind.

Our bodies are designed to squat in poses like Frog pose. In parts of the world where squatting is common in everyday life, people rarely suffer from back pain. Unfortunately many people around the world have lost the ability to squat comfortably because they spend so much time sitting in chairs. The muscles at the back of their legs, called hamstrings, become tight and their back muscles weaken, which can lead to backache. Squat in Frog pose every day and keep your legs and back as healthy as possible.

F

G is for Giraffe
(Prasarita Paddotanasana)

Benefits:

Stretches your legs and back

Strengthens your feet, ankles and legs

Twists your spine and maintains the normal mobility of your spinal muscles

Calms your mind

Affirmation:

I am expansive.

1. Stand with your feet wide apart and facing forwards.

2. Breathe in and stretch your arms wide to the sides.

3. Breathe out and fold forwards at your hips.

4. Bring your left hand to your right leg or ankle.

5. Lift your right hand up to the sky, twist to the right, look up at your right hand.

6. Breathe in and out a few times.

7. Repeat on the other side.

8. Stand up and step your feet together.

 Imagine you are a giraffe and that the arm you reach upwards is your neck and your hand is your mouth. Imagine you are reaching up for leaves on a tall acacia tree that is almost out of your reach.

Reflections

Giraffes are the tallest animals on earth. They have long, stilt-like legs and purple-black tongues that help them pull leaves and thorns from the treetops. They have seven bones called vertebrae in their necks. This is exactly the same number of vertebrae that you have in your neck.

H is for Happy Baby
(Ananda Balasana)

Benefits:

Stretches and releases tension in your hips, legs and groin

Calms your mind

Affirmation:

I am joyful.

1. Lie on your back.

2. Hook your first two fingers around your big toes or hold your feet.

3. Gently pull on your feet so your knees come towards the floor on either side of your body.

4. Try to keep your lower back pressed onto the floor.

5. Breathe deeply a few times.

6. Move your legs around and feel movement in your hip joints.

 Imagine you are a baby again! Feel carefree, happy and playful. You don't have a trouble in the world. When you feel stressed, tired or anxious come into Happy Baby pose.

Reflections

Babies are natural yogis. Watch how they come into Happy Baby pose without any need for tuition. Maybe you have pictures of yourself as a baby in this pose.

I is for Icicle (variation of Tadasana)

Benefits:

Strengthens your arms, shoulders and back

Encourages good posture

Calms and focuses your mind

Affirmation:

I am beautiful.

1. Stand with your feet together.

2. Lift your hands into a prayer pose above your head and relax your shoulders.

3. Breathe in and out a few times.

 Icicles are hanging spikes of ice formed by the freezing of dripping water. Close your eyes and imagine you are a beautiful icicle sparkling in the sunshine. Feel as if your body is hanging from your fingers and lengthening. Relax your shoulders and jaw. Notice if you tend to clench your teeth. If you do, try to make space between your back teeth.

Adjustment

Stand behind the person in Icicle. Place your hands on their shoulders and encourage them to soften and relax them.

J is for Jellyfish

Benefits:

Strengthens your
core muscles

Calms your mind and
relieves anxiety

Affirmation:

I am free.

1. Lie on your back.

2. Lift your arms and legs, move them as if they are tentacles.

3. Bend and straighten your arms and legs.

4. Breathe in and out a few times.

 Imagine you are a jellyfish. Close your eyes and visualise yourself drifting through the ocean. Allow yourself to move with the current. Picture the colours of the water around you. Float and move freely. You have no plan, no agenda. You can simply be yourself and drift along. Breathe slowly and enjoy feeling free in your body. Immerse yourself in the present moment.

Reflections

There is a species of jellyfish called *Turritopsis nutricula* that is known as the immortal jellyfish as it is able to regenerate its own cells. As long as it is not eaten or it doesn't catch a disease, it theoretically could live forever.

J

K is for Kite

Benefits:

Strengthens your legs

Stretches your arms
and shoulders

Affirmation:

I am light and carefree.

1. Stand with your feet together.

2. Bend your right knee and lift your right foot towards your bottom.

3. Reach back and hold onto your right foot with both your hands.

4. Lift your right foot up and back so it is pressing into your hands.

5. Breathe in and out a few times.

6. Repeat on the other side.

 Imagine you are a kite flying high in the sky. Imagine your standing leg is the rope tethering you to the ground and your upper body is the kite floating high up in the sky. Feel grounded to the earth through your standing foot and lift up through your spine and through the crown of your head. Feel a stretch at the front of the thigh of your lifted leg and keep your pelvis in a neutral position so you don't overarch your lower back.

Variation

Try reaching one arm alongside your head or holding one arm by the side of your body. Keep hold of your raised foot with the other hand.

Guided meditation

'Lie on your back and close your eyes. Imagine a kite dancing way above you in the sky. Imagine what colour it is. Imagine how it moves. The wind takes it far, far away from you.

Your mind is often like the kite, far away from your body.

Now imagine you are reeling the kite in, so it is coming closer and closer to your body. At the same time bring your awareness to your body and breath.

Breathe in as you bring your kite down and breathe out as you bring your awareness to yourself.

Rest your hands on your belly and feel it lifting up as you breathe in and feel it moving down as you breathe out.

Keep your awareness in your body and with your breath. Notice what your body feels like right now. Feel the ground beneath you and be aware where your body is connecting with the ground. Feel the touch of the air on your skin. Feel the touch of your clothes on your skin. Feel your body moving gently with each breath you take in and out.

If your thoughts wander away from your body and your breath, imagine a kite again, flying high in the sky, and reel it back in. Keep bringing your awareness back to yourself. When you are ready, slowly open your eyes.'

L is for Lion (Simhasana)

Benefits:

Stretches and relaxes your face and jaw.

Helps you to become aware of your feelings and teaches you that your feelings never last.

Helps you to be mindful of unpleasant feelings and to be patient as they pass.

Teaches you to respond thoughtfully rather than reacting instantly to your feelings.

1. Kneel with your hands on your knees.

2. Breathe in deeply.

3. Stick out your tongue towards your chin, open your mouth wide, look up and breathe out loudly.

4. Close your mouth, close your eyes and breathe in gently and calmly.

5. Repeat five times.

 Imagine you are a roaring lion on the plains of Africa. You are strong and wild. How does this feel? Shake your head and move your body like a lion. Feel natural and free.

Affirmation:

I am aware of myself,
I accept how I feel and I
know my feelings will pass.

Reflections

Feelings come and go. They never last. When you are doing Lion pose be aware of how you feel right now. Sometimes our feelings are mixed up and we can feel many things at once. This is very natural and you can use Lion pose to help you become more aware of and accepting of all your different feelings.

Breathing to calm down

Think of all the feelings that you enjoy – happiness, excitement, peace, relaxation, safety. Then think of all the feelings that are more difficult – anger, fear, sadness, jealousy, confusion or disappointment.

The best way to deal with unpleasant feelings is to accept them, rather than trying to push them away. In yoga we remember that peace and happiness are always inside us, even if it feels like our difficult emotions are overwhelming us. We know that eventually our feelings will pass away.

When you feel angry, rather than immediately acting on your anger and doing something that you will regret later, try saying this to yourself as you breathe deeply in and out in Lion pose:

'I breathe in and I know I feel angry

I breathe out and I know that anger doesn't feel good

I breathe in and I know that this feeling won't last

I breathe out and I help myself to feel calmer'

You can use the same technique, which is inspired by Thich Nhat Hanh's teachings on mindfulness, when you are feeling other unpleasant emotions.

As you feel yourself calming down, you can start to think about or talk to someone you trust about what it is that is making you feel angry, frightened, sad or disappointed. As you look at the cause of your unpleasant feelings it will help you to understand them and this will eventually help you to transform them into something more positive – forgiveness, acceptance, determination, peace, strength, resilience and courage.

M is for Mouse (Balasana)

Benefits:

Stretches and lengthens your spine

Stretches your feet, ankles, legs and hips

Relieves stress and anxiety

Encourages slow, calm breathing

Settles you when you feel overtired or overwrought

Helps you sleep

Affirmation:

I am safe.

1. Kneel with your legs and feet together.

2. Rest your bottom on your heels.

3. Fold your upper body over your thighs.

4. Rest your forehead on the ground.

5. Rest your arms by the sides of your body with your palms facing up.

6. Close your eyes, breathe slowly and stay in the pose for as long as you want to.

 Imagine you are a quiet, gentle mouse. You are curled up and feel safe. Breathe slowly and enjoy feeling relaxed.

Breathing to focus and concentrate

Close your eyes in Mouse and count ten slow, gentle breaths, saying 'in-out-one', 'in-out-two', 'in-out-three' and so on up to ten. Say 'in' as you breathe in and 'out' as you breathe out. Notice how you feel before and after this practice. Try to do it once in the morning and once in the evening. Learn to be very comfortable with yourself and your breath.

Notice how easy it is for your mind to become distracted and your thoughts to wander during this practice. This is very natural as our human minds are usually very scattered and busy. Keep coming back to an awareness of your breath and over time you will improve your ability to focus on one thing. The ability to concentrate is a wonderful skill to have through your life.

Adjustment

Ask a friend or a sibling to carefully lie on your back when you are in Mouse pose. Keep talking to each other to make sure you are comfortable. Stay in the pose if it feels good but let your friend or sibling know as soon as you want them to get off! If you are doing this, you need to communicate really well with each other. You can also try lying on your parent's back when they are in Mouse pose.

When your child is in Mouse, place your hands on their upper back and ask them to feel their back expanding into your hands every time they breathe in and relaxing down as they breathe out. This gentle practice will help to reassure them, particularly before they fall asleep or when they are upset.

Variation

Reach your arms forward and rest them on the ground with your palms facing up or down. Keep your shoulders relaxed.

N is for Namasté

Benefits:

Encourages good posture

Develops self awareness

Calms your mind

Affirmation:

I am grateful and protected.

1. Sit, stand, kneel or lie (in your bed if you want). Whatever feels best for you right now.

2. Bring your hands into a prayer position in front of your chest.

3. Close your eyes, breathe steadily and stay in the pose for as long as you want to.

 Imagine a world that is peaceful and harmonious.

Reflections

This pose reminds us to be grateful. What do you feel grateful for? Your family, the food you eat, a roof over your head, the sunshine, friends, kindness – there is so much you can be grateful for.

The pose also helps us to feel protected, safe, peaceful and calm. What do you need to protect yourself from?

At the end of a yoga class we bring our hands into a prayer position and say 'Namasté' to each other. By doing this, we are showing that we care for and respect each other and ourselves. We are demonstrating that the goodness in ourselves recognises the goodness in others.

Breathing to increase awareness

Close your eyes in Namasté and count ten slow, gentle breaths, saying 'in-out-one', 'in-out-two', 'in-out-three' and so on up to ten. Say 'in' as you breathe in and 'out' as you breathe out. Notice how you feel before and after this practice. Try to do it once in the morning and once in the evening. Learn to be very comfortable with yourself and your breath.

O is for Oyster

Benefits:

Synchronises your breath with your movements

Stretches and strengthens your arms, shoulders and back

Calms and focuses your mind

Affirmation:

I am positive.

1. Stand or sit with your hands in a prayer position in front of your chest.

2. Breathe in and lift your hands above your head in prayer position.

3. Breathe out and move your arms wide out to the sides as if drawing a circle around yourself.

4. Bring your arms by your sides and then bring your hands back to prayer position in front of your chest.

5. Repeat four times.

6. Reverse the direction and repeat four times.

 Imagine you are an oyster on the seabed. Sometimes a grain of sand gets between an oyster's shell and its skin. This irritates the oyster. So it makes a pearly material to surround the grain of sand. In this way, over a few years, a pearl is formed. Imagine a beautiful pearl inside your oyster shell.

Reflections

Think of something that makes you feel irritated, worried, angry, sad, frightened or doubtful. As you circle your arms around your body imagine you are like the oyster, slowly yet surely transforming what is troubling you into something beautiful and positive. You have the power to transform negative thoughts into ones that are positive, protective and useful. It takes tolerance, focus and attention but it is always possible.

If you spend lots of time sitting at a desk or at a computer do Oyster to release tension in your arms, shoulders and back.

Breathing to reassure and settle you

If your child is struggling to control their feelings, words and actions, invite them to sit or stand opposite you. Place the palms of your hands gently on the palms of your child and look kindly into their eyes. Ask them to breathe in and lift their arms so you are mirroring each other's movements while holding your palms together. Ask them to breathe out and circle their arms wide to the sides, again so you are mirroring each other. Keep your palms touching as you move and breathe in and out at the same time. Do four circles in each direction, or more if you prefer. This is a very beautiful, reassuring practice to share with your child.

P is for Pigeon (Kapotasana)

Benefits:

Increases your hip flexibility

Opens your chest and encourages you to breathe well

Develops and maintains the flexibility of your spine

Builds your confidence

Affirmation:

I am comfortable with myself.

1. Come onto your hands and knees.

2. Slide your right knee between your hands and angle it slightly to the right, and slide your right shin forwards.

3. Straighten your left leg behind you.

4. Press your hands on the floor on either side of you.

5. Gently lift your chest and arch your upper back.

6. Breathe in and out a few times.

7. Repeat on the other side.

 Imagine you are a pigeon as you lift your chest.

Reflections

Like eagles, pigeons are very intelligent birds. They have been used to carry messages for centuries because of their natural homing instincts.

Use your yoga practice to know who you are and to feel secure, strong and comfortable with yourself. Breathe steadily and come home to a peaceful place within yourself, regardless of what is happening in the world around you. You will find this a useful skill, both now and throughout your life.

Q is for Queen Cleopatra

Benefits:

Synchronises your movements with your breath

Encourages good posture

Releases tension in your shoulders and neck, particularly after studying at a desk or computer

Affirmation:

I am fearless.

1. Sit, stand or kneel.

2. Bend your elbows, place your hands at the back of your head and link your fingers together.

3. Breathe in.

4. Breathe out and turn your head to the right.

5. Breathe in and bring your head back to the centre.

6. Breathe out and turn your head to the left.

7. Breathe in and bring your head back to the centre.

8. Repeat five times.

 Cleopatra was known as the Queen of the Nile. She was a brilliant, fearless character and a powerful communicator. It is said she spoke up to twelve languages. Imagine you are Queen Cleopatra of Egypt. Feel strong and powerful as you stand tall and turn your head from side to side.

Reflections

As you turn your head in Queen Cleopatra think about what you are fearful of. What does your fear prevent you from doing? Have courage to be yourself and to take positive action in the world.

Your neck is the most flexible part of your spine, which makes it the most vulnerable to injury.

Stress and tension can build up here, particularly if you spend a lot of time on a computer or phone, at a desk or if you are anxious and worried. Queen Cleopatra pose will help you to be more aware of your neck so you can release tension and keep it relaxed, healthy and comfortable.

R is for Rabbit (Sasangasana)

Benefits:

Calms your mind

Stretches your back, neck, arms and shoulders

Relieves anxiety and sadness

Encourages a positive attitude

Promotes good sleep

Affirmation:

I am quiet.

1. Come into Mouse pose (see page 70).

2. Hold your heels.

3. Tuck your chin towards your chest.

4. Carefully lower your forehead to the floor.

5. Lift your hips and bottom.

6. Breathe in and out a few times.

7. Rest in Mouse pose.

 Imagine you are a quiet, gentle rabbit, safe in your warren. Feel protected and peaceful.

Breathing to let go of troubles and anxieties

As you breathe in say the word 'Let' and as you breathe out, say the word 'Go'. You can do this silently or out loud. Repeat this ten times.

As you breathe in, be aware if you are feeling worried about anything. As you breathe out, let go of your troubles and anxieties.

Variation

Try gently placing the crown (top) of your head on the floor. If the stretch for your back is too strong then keep your forehead on the floor. Always listen to your body and do what is best for you.

Reflections

If you ever feel you are holding the weight of the world on your shoulders, use the Rabbit pose to help you to let go of your responsibilities and to feel free. Trust that everything will work out well and that there is a solution for every problem.

S is for Snail

Benefits:

Stretches your back

Strengthens your upper body

Affirmation:

I am slow, sure and purposeful.

1. Lie on your front with your hands on the ground, your wrists under your shoulders, your palms flat and your elbows bent and tucked into your sides.

2. Curl your toes under.

3. Bend your knees and lift your bottom up.

4. Breathe in and out a few times.

5. Relax on your front.

 Imagine you are a snail and that the lifted part of your body is your shell.

Breathing to feel strong and confident

When snails are frightened they retreat into their shells to protect themselves. What do you do when you are scared?

The next time you are facing a situation that makes you feel afraid try this breathing exercise to help you feel calm, strong and brave. Take a deep breath in for two counts and a long breath out for four counts. Do this five times.

Notice how the way you breathe can help to change the way you feel. Your breath is your friend and you can use it to help you through many situations in life.

T is for Tree (Vrikshasana)

Benefits:

Strengthens your legs and feet

Stretches your inner thigh and groin

Improves your balance

Develops your focus, concentration and confidence

Relieves anxiety

Affirmation:

I am grounded.

1. Stand with your feet together.

2. Lift your right foot to the inside of your right thigh (or the inside of your lower leg if easier).

3. Bring your hands into a prayer pose in front of your chest and then above your head.

4. Balance for as long as you can. Keep your eyes focused on something straight ahead of you to help you balance.

5. When you are ready to come out of the pose, bring your hands in prayer position in front of your chest and then by the sides of your body.

6. Lower your right foot to the ground.

7. Repeat on the other side.

 Imagine you are a tree growing tall and strong. Imagine what type of tree you are and what season it is.

Reflections

Trees make oxygen, which we breathe in and need to stay alive. We breathe out carbon dioxide, which trees need to stay alive. When you're in the Tree pose remember to breathe in and out deeply and remember how important it is that we protect the Earth's forests. When we work together with nature, everything is in harmony.

The best place to practise Tree pose is in a forest, garden or park, among the beautiful trees. If possible take off your shoes and socks and feel the earth beneath your feet.

Once you can balance well in Tree pose, try closing your eyes. When your eyes are closed you need to be very aware of your body and your mind needs to be calm and focused in order to balance.

Variation

Hold hands with your siblings, parents and friends in Tree pose and imagine you are a great forest. You could be an ancient oak wood, a tropical rainforest, a snowy mountain forest, a bluebell wood in spring or palm trees on the beach. You can do this standing in a circle. Notice how stable and strong you are in Tree pose when you are holding hands and supporting each other.

U is for Upward Facing Dog
(Urdhva Mukha Svanasana)

Benefits:

Strengthens legs, back, wrists, arms and shoulders

Develops and maintains flexibility of spine

Opens chest and encourages deep breathing

1. Lie on your front with your hands on the ground, your wrists under your shoulders, your palms flat and your elbows bent and tucked into your sides.

2. Straighten your arms and lift your body off the ground so you are only resting on your palms and the tops of your feet.

3. Gently arch back and look up.

4. Breathe in and out a few times.

5. Rest in Mouse pose (see page 70).

Affirmation:

I am determined.

 Imagine you are a dog stretching its body after a long sleep. How do you like to stretch when you wake up in the morning?

Reflections

This pose requires a lot of strength. Don't worry if you can't lift your whole body off the floor. Keep practising and you'll get there. Learn to have a goal and to take small, consistent steps towards realising it.

U

V is for Volcano

Benefits:

Stretches and strengthens legs and arms

Affirmation:

I am powerful.

1. Stand with your feet hip-width apart.

2. Squat down and touch the ground with your fingers.

3. Jump up and reach your hands as high as you can.

4. Repeat a few times.

 As you jump up, imagine you are an exploding volcano. When you leap in the air you can make any shapes you want to with your body. Feel the power of your body uncoiling as you lift up.

Reflections

When you have been sitting for a long time, at a desk or in a car, you can energise your body and clear your mind by squatting and then leaping high in Volcano pose. Feel the power of your body uncoiling as you lift up and see how many shapes you can make in the air.

Breathing to cool down

If you are feeling hot and bothered, try this breathing exercise to help yourself feel cooler and calmer. Breathe in through your nose and then blow air out slowly and steadily through your mouth, making a gentle breeze that would make a candle flicker but would not blow it out completely. Do this five times.

W is for Wheel (Chakrasana)

Benefits:

Strengthens your arms, legs and core

Develops and maintains your spine flexibility

Opens your chest and encourages you to breathe well

Builds your confidence and stamina

1. Lie on your back with your feet flat on the ground and hip-width apart.

2. Place your palms flat on the ground on either side of your head.

3. Lift up onto your hands and feet.

4. Straighten your arms and legs as much as you can.

5. Breathe in and out a few times.

6. Lower yourself onto the ground.

7. Hug your knees to your chest and relax.

Affirmation:

I am aware and flexible.

 Imagine you are a wheel and feel the curve of your arms, torso and legs. Feel strong, flexible and relaxed, all at once.

Variations

Make beautiful rainbows in Wheel pose with your family and friends. The tallest person comes into Wheel. The next tallest person comes into Wheel underneath them. Continue in size order, with as many of you that can fit into the rainbow.

Imagine you are a rainbow in the sky and visualise which colour each one of you is – violet, indigo, blue, green, yellow, orange or red. When you are ready to come out of the pose, the person at the bottom lowers down and moves away, one at a time.

Reflections

Rainbows are formed when the sun shines through drops of water, which act as prisms splitting the light into different colours.

Creating rainbows in Wheel will strengthen the relationships between the individuals that make up your family. The Rainbow requires you to communicate carefully with each other and to make sure that everyone is happy and safe.

X is for X Marks the Spot

Benefits:

Stretches your arms and legs

Affirmation:

I am precious.

1. Lie on your back.
2. Stretch your arms and legs out to the sides and make an X shape.
3. Breathe in and out a few times.

 Imagine you are the X on a map marking the place where treasure is buried. Imagine what treasure you would like to find.

Reflections

Think of what you treasure the most in your life. Your family and friends. Your home. Your favourite toys. Clean air to breathe. Our beautiful world.

Breathing to calm down

Lie in the pose and close your eyes. Feel your belly and your chest lifting up and down as you breathe in and out. Enjoy lying still, breathing deeply and mindfully.

Y is for Yoga

Benefits:

Strengthens your arms, shoulders and back

Improves your posture

Affirmation:

I am relaxed, strong and focused.

1. Stand with your feet together.

2. Lift your arms on either side of your head to make a Y shape.

3. Breathe in and out a few times.

 Imagine you are the letter Y. How many different ways can you make a Y shape with your body? How many other letter shapes can you make with your body?

Breathing and balancing to focus and energise

Stand tall in the pose. Breathe in and lift your heels up high. Breathe out and lower your heels down. Do this three times. Then lift your heels and hold the balance for three counts, whilst holding your breath. Breathe out and slowly lower your heels down. Do this three times. Look at a still point straight ahead of you to help balance. Notice how this breathing and balancing exercise helps you feel strong, steady, stable and calm.

Z is for Zig Zag Twist

Benefits:

Stretches your back muscles

Energises you

Opens your chest and encourages you to breathe well

Supports your digestion and can help relieve constipation

Affirmation:

I am open.

1. Lie on your back with your arms stretched out wide to the sides and your palms facing up.

2. Bend your knees to your chest.

3. Breathe in.

4. Breathe out, lower your knees to the floor on the right and turn your head to look along your left arm.

5. Breathe steadily five times.

6. Breathe in and lift your knees and head to the starting position.

7. Breathe out, lower your knees to the floor on the left and turn your head to look along your right arm.

8. Breathe steadily five times.

9. Breathe in and lift your knees and head to the starting position.

 Close your eyes and imagine the Z shape of your body in this pose. Feel the shape of your spine in this pose and when you return to the starting position. Be aware of the natural curves of your spine when you are in a resting position.

Reflection

When you were born your spine was a C-shape. As you learned to lift your head the curve of your neck developed. Then as you learned to sit up, crawl, stand and walk, the curve in your lower back developed. Your spine can move into so many wonderful shapes and positions. As you grow up it's important to keep your spine flexible and healthy by moving it gently in all the different ways you can. Practising Zig Zag Twist with your family is a wonderful way to do that.

One more pose: Savasana

Benefits:

Rests your mind and body

Reassures you

Calms and balances your nervous system

Affirmation:

I am at peace.

1. At the end or the beginning of your yoga practice, lie on your back and close your eyes.

2. Either straighten your legs and lie them hip-width apart or bend your knees and rest your feet flat on the ground – whatever is most comfortable and natural for your body.

3. Rest your palms on your belly either side of your tummy button, or rest your arms by your sides with your palms facing the sky.

4. Close your eyes and breathe steadily in and out.

Breathing for peace and quiet

Breathe in and out softly through your nose. Place your hands on your belly and feel where your body is moving when you breathe in and out. Feel your belly gently rise when you breathe in and gently move back down when you breathe out. Be aware where your body moves when you breathe in and where it moves when you breathe out.

Reflection

Savasana is the most important of all the yoga positions. How easy is it for you to lie still and allow yourself to rest?

The A-Z of Yoga game

W hen you have learned all the yoga poses from A–Z you can play this game. It's the first thing the children in my yoga classes ask to play. Even the teenagers! It teaches younger children their alphabet and an impressive range of yoga poses. They also improve their memory as well as learning to focus and concentrate.

Sit or stand in a circle. Take it in turns to come into a yoga pose starting with the letter A, then B, then C. Continue through the alphabet. If you can't think of a pose then you are out of the game and the next person has to think of a pose beginning with that letter. The winner is the last player left in the game.

You can team younger children up with older children or adults to help them out.

The Detective Yoga game

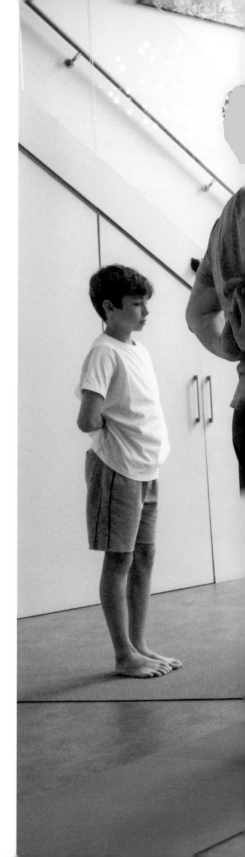

This is another favourite in my yoga classes. It will teach you to move slowly, with control, care and patience. It will also teach you to work well as a team, by paying close attention to each other.

Sit or stand in a circle and choose one person to be the Detective. The Detective leaves the room and the remaining players choose a Leader. The Leader chooses the first pose for everyone to come into. When the Detective comes back into the room they must stand in the middle of the circle. The Leader changes the yoga pose at various intervals and the other children copy it as subtly as possible so the Detective doesn't guess the identity of the Leader. Once the team has come into five different poses the Detective's job is to guess the identity of the Leader. The winner is the person who guesses the identity of the Leader in the least amount of attempts.

When children are new to yoga it's a good idea to give the Leader a list of poses to move through, along with pictures to remind them of what to do.

The Sun Salutation sequence
(Start your day together)

T he Sun Salutation (Surya Namaskar) is a classic, flowing sequence of yoga poses and is the perfect way to start the day with your family. It is easy to learn and will make you feel energised, relaxed and focused, as you stretch and strengthen your body.

Traditionally you do twelve rounds (six on each side), while facing the rising sun in the east. You can try it indoors or out, facing each other, looking at an inspiring view or even facing eastward. Do as many rounds as you have the energy and time for. Move slowly and mindfully and, most importantly, enjoy spending time together.

1. Mountain

Stand at the front of your mat with your feet together and your arms by your sides.

2. Namasté

Bring your hands into a prayer position in front of your chest.

3. Icicle

Lift your hands in prayer position above your head and relax your shoulders.

4. Rag Doll

Fold forwards, either with your legs straight or your knees slightly bent.

5. Horse

On the first round, step your right foot as far back as you can, lower your right knee to the ground and lift your chest and face. On the second round, step your left foot back, lower your left knee to the ground and lift your chest and face. On each subsequent round, alternate between your right and left feet.

6. Plank

Step your other foot back so you are in a press up position with a flat back and your chest above the space between your hands.

7. Snail

Lower down onto your knees, chest and chin. Tuck your elbows into your sides and lift your bottom up.

8. Cobra

Lower down onto your front. Place your palms flat on the ground and lift your chest and face without putting any weight on your hands.

9. Downward Dog

Curl your toes under, press into your hands, lift your bottom up and press your heels towards the ground.

10. Horse

On the first round, step your right foot forwards and lower your left knee to the ground. On the second round, step your left foot forwards and lower your right knee.

11. Rag Doll

Step your feet together and hang forwards.

12. Icicle

Lift your hands in prayer position above your head and relax your shoulders.

13. Namasté

Bring your hands into a prayer position in front of your chest.

14. Mountain

Stand at the front of your mat with your feet together and your arms by your sides.

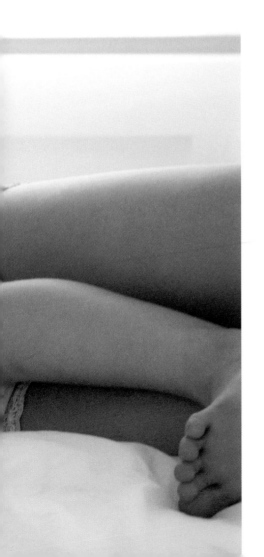

The Yoga in Bed sequence

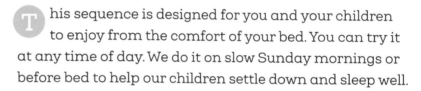

T his sequence is designed for you and your children to enjoy from the comfort of your bed. You can try it at any time of day. We do it on slow Sunday mornings or before bed to help our children settle down and sleep well.

The sequence will move your spine in four different ways – forward-bending, back-bending, twisting and side-bending. Talk to your children about how it feels to move your spine in different ways and explain that if they do these poses every day they will keep the natural flexibility and health of their spine, now and in the future.

"This sequence will help your children to settle down and sleep well."

Relaxation

1. Lie on your back, place your hands on your tummy and close your eyes.

2. Listen to the sounds outside your room (for a few seconds).

3. Listen to the sounds inside your room (for a few seconds).

4. Listen to the sound of your breathing (for a few seconds).

5. As you breathe in feel your tummy rising up.

6. As you breathe out feel your tummy moving down.

7. Feel the natural movement of your tummy as you breathe in and out.

8. Smile to yourself.

9. Feel happy and grateful.

Explain to your child that being mindful is noticing what your body feels like, how you are breathing, what thoughts you are having, what sounds you can hear and what is going on around you, right now. Helping your child to be mindful is a gift you are giving them for life.

Crescent Moon

1. Lie on your back, bring your arms up on either side of your head.

2. Keep your legs and pelvis still.

3. Bend your upper body to the right.

4. Breathe in and out four times.

5. Return to the starting point.

6. Bend your upper body to the left.

7. Breathe in and out four times.

8. Return to the starting point.

As you bend to each side imagine you are the moon reflecting the light of the sun towards the Earth. From the moon you can watch the Earth spinning in space. It is your home and will be the home of your children and the children of your children. What can you, your family and your school do to protect the Earth?

Crescent Moon can also be done in a standing position. Stand with your feet together, hold your hands above your head in prayer position, link your fingers together, point your index fingers towards the sky and gently bend from side to side.

Explain to your child that they are side-bending their spine.

Zig Zag Twist

1. Lie on your back and bend your knees to your chest.

2. Stretch your arms wide to the sides with your palms facing up.

3. Lower your knees to the right and turn your face to the left.

4. Breathe in and out four times.

5. Return to the starting point.

6. Lower your knees to the left and turn your face to the right.

7. Breathe in and out four times.

8. Return to the starting point.

Explain to your child that they are twisting their spine.

Ball

1. Lie on your back and bend your knees to your chest.

2. Place your hands on your knees.

3. Breathe in.

4. Breathe out and curl up, lift your head, shoulders, bottom and lower back.

5. Breathe in and lower yourself down.

6. Repeat four times.

Explain to your child that they are flexing their spine.

Bridge

1. Lie on your back with your knees bent, feet flat and hip-width apart.

2. Bring your arms by your side with your palms facing down.

3. Breathe in and lift your bottom, lower back and hips up.

4. Breathe out and lower yourself back down.

5. Repeat four times.

Explain to your child that they are extending their spine.

Reclining Tree

1. Lie on your back, bend your left knee and place your left foot on the inside of your right thigh.

2. Bring your hands into prayer pose in front of your chest or on the ground above your head.

3. Breathe in and out four times

4. Repeat on the other side

Ask your child to relax their shoulders and to notice if the pose feels different on each side.

Butterfly

1. Lie down or sit up.

2. Bend your knees and bring the soles of your feet together.

3. If you are sitting up hold onto your feet.

4. If you are lying down place your hands on your inner thighs.

5. Breathe in and out four times.

Mouse

1. Close your eyes in Mouse pose (page 70).

2. Breathe in and out four times.

3. Imagine you are a quiet, gentle mouse. Imagine you are curled up and are feeling safe and sound. Breathe slowly and enjoy being still. Let yourself relax deeply.

4. If you are doing the sequence in the morning make a positive goal for your day ahead. Repeat it three times to yourself. Then sit up and open your eyes.

5. If it is bedtime then curl up in your bed in a comfortable position. Feel safe and sleep well.

Partner yoga

T here is always laughter in our house or in my children's yoga classes when we do partner yoga!

These poses will strengthen the relationship between you and your children, encouraging you all to be light in body and lighthearted in mind.

The poses require you to communicate clearly with each other, sometimes verbally and other times without words. Talk to your children about how effective and successful they are when they work with each other and cooperate well with their family and friends.

"Partner yoga will strengthen the relationship between you and your children, encouraging you all to be light in body and lighthearted in mind."

Sailing Boats

1. Sit facing each other, bend your knees, touch your toes and hold hands.

2. Lift your right legs up and press your soles together.

3. Lift your left legs up and press your soles together.

4. Straighten your legs and carefully lean back.

5. Imagine you are sailing boats floating on the sea.

6. Smile at each other as you balance.

Lizard on the Rock

1. Choose who will be the Rock and who will be the Lizard.

2. If you are the Rock, come into Mouse pose.

3. If you are the Lizard, gently lean back over the Rock and place your hands on the ground on either side of their head.

4. Imagine you are a lizard lying on a rock, warming yourself in the sun, or imagine you are a rock on the beach.

5. Adjust the pose so you are both comfortable.

6. Breathe gently and relax together.

7. When you are ready to come out of the pose the Lizard lifts up into Wheel pose and the Rock escapes.

8. Swap over and repeat the pose.

Big Dog Little Dog

1. Choose who will be the Big Dog and who will be the Little Dog.

2. If you are Big Dog, come into Downward Dog pose.

3. If you are Little Dog, stand in front of Big Dog and come into Rag Doll pose.

4. If you are Little Dog carefully place one foot on Big Dog's lower back (sacrum) and then the other foot.

5. Big Dog creates a firm foundation and Little Dog presses gently on Big Dog's lower back.

6. Communicate well and make sure you are both comfortable.

7. Carefully come out of the pose, swap over and repeat the pose.

Chairs

1. Stand facing each other and hold hands.

2. Carefully lean back and hold each other's weight.

3. Slowly bend your knees and slowly lower down until you are sitting on imaginary chairs.

4. Stand up again slowly while leaning away from each other.

5. Smile at each other as you move down and up.

6. You can also try bending all the way down into a squatting position.

7. Try Chair pose on your own by sitting in an imaginary chair with your arms raised on either side of your head.

Mountain Peaks

1. Face each other, lift your arms, press your palms together and slowly step away from each other.

2. Lean forwards and push your hands up high, so you are holding each other up.

3. Imagine you are Mount Everest, the tallest mountain on earth. Feel firmly grounded through your feet as you reach up high into the clouds.

4. Smile at each other.

5. If you are much taller than your partner, you can try kneeling.

Hibernating Bear in a Cave

1. Choose who will be the Bear and who will be the Cave.

2. If you are the Cave, come into Downward Dog or Plank pose.

3. If you are the Bear, come into Mouse pose.

4. If you are the Bear, imagine you are deeply asleep and safe in your cave during the winter months.

5. If you are the Cave, imagine you are creating a place where the Bear is protected and can rest well.

6. You can choose to be another hibernating creature – perhaps a tortoise or a hedgehog. You can also imagine you are a gate or a door as you hold Downward Dog and allow your children to crawl under you.

Porridge

1. Sit with your child between your legs and both spread your legs wide.

2. Imagine you are stirring a bowl of porridge or a potion together.

3. Chat about what you are making.

Story time

Acting out your children's favourite stories using yoga poses is a wonderful activity to do with younger children. Read the story first and then retell it while coming into the relevant yoga poses. If there isn't a specific yoga pose for a character or object in the book then you can make it up. Encourage your children to be creative and inventive!

To start you off here is a classic story – **Goldilocks and the Three Bears**. The yoga poses for each character or object are in brackets.

Once upon a time there was a little girl called Goldilocks (**Namasté**).

One beautiful summer's day she went for a walk in the forest (**Tree**).

As she wandered along she saw butterflies fluttering around her (**Butterfly**).

She also heard frogs croaking in the pond (**Frog**) and felt very happy.

Then she saw a cottage with a door (**Downward Dog**) surrounded by roses. She smelled a delicious smell that she couldn't resist, so she walked right in! Let your children crawl under you as you hold Downward Dog!

Inside she found three bowls of porridge (**Porridge**). She tried the big bowl but it was too hot. She tried the medium-sized bowl but it was too cold. She tried the little bowl and it was delicious, so she ate it all up!

She was feeling a little tired when she saw three chairs (**Chair**).

The big chair was too hard. The medium-sized chair was too soft. The little chair was just right. She settled down but the chair broke (fall over from **Chair**).

She picked herself up and wandered upstairs, where she found three beds (**Bed**).

The big bed was too hard. The medium-sized bed was too lumpy. The little bed was just right.

She fell fast asleep (encourage your children to close their eyes in **Relaxation pose**).

As Goldilocks was sleeping the three bears, who owned the cottage, arrived home.

'Someone's been eating my porridge' growled the Daddy Bear.

'Someone's been eating my porridge' growled the Mummy Bear.

'Someone's been eating my porridge' cried the Baby Bear. 'And they've eaten it all up!' (**Porridge**)

'Someone's been sitting on my chair' growled Daddy Bear. (**Chair**)

'Someone's been sitting on my chair' growled Mummy Bear.

'Someone's been sitting on my chair' cried the Baby Bear. 'And they've broken it!'

The three bears heard a noise upstairs and went to investigate.

'Someone's been sleeping in my bed' growled Daddy Bear. (**Bed**)

'Someone's been sleeping in my bed' growled Mummy Bear.

'Someone's been sleeping in my bed' cried the Baby Bear. 'And she's still there!'

The three bears growled at Goldilocks (**Lion**).

She woke up, leapt out of bed, ran out of the house (let your children crawl under you again as you hold **Downward Dog**)

and into the Forest (**Tree**).

Goldilocks never returned to the house of the three bears again (**Namasté**).

Yoga and your family

A family yoga practice, however simple, will give you precious moments with your children, which will sustain you all, both now and in the future.

Every day your children grow. Every day your children change. It is easy to get caught up in the rush of being a caregiver to them and to miss the miracle of childhood as it unfolds. Yoga will bring you back to the reality of each present moment, connecting you with the joy and peace that is always within you and around you.

'Take the hand of your child and invite him or her to go out and sit with you on the grass. The two of you may want to contemplate the green grass, the little flowers that grow among the grasses, and the sky. Breathing and smiling together – that is peace education. If we know how to appreciate these beautiful things, we will not have to search for anything else. Peace is available in every moment, in every breath, in every step.'

Thich Nhat Hanh

Acknowledgements

Thank you to my family, friends and teachers for your love and constant support.

Thank you to Vanessa Berberian for capturing the calm beauty of yoga in your photographs.

Thank you to Alba, Taliyah, Vrinda, Veyllan, Vanessa, Ceki, Marcelo, Amalya, Lior, Tess, Max, Alex, Kumi, Kei, Alyssa, Dylan, Kai, Rafferty and Florence for patiently expressing the grace of each yoga pose.

Thank you to Allan for his considered design. Thank you to Martin, Zoë, Susan and Antonia at YogaWords for their generous spirit and for making the process of publishing this book a joy.

Thank you to Françoise Freedman at Birthlight, to Manizeh, Emily, Dannii, Huma, Cat & Phil at Sangyé Yoga and to Bala & Pawan at Shreya's Yoga Retreat for sharing the wisdom and light of yoga.